Can I Have a Dragon?

'Can I Have a Dragon?'

An original concept by Elizabeth Dale

© Elizabeth Dale

Illustrated by Ellie O'Shea

Published by MAVERICK ARTS PUBLISHING LTD

Studio 11, City Business Centre, 6 Brighton Road,

Horsham, West Sussex, RH13 5BB

© Maverick Arts Publishing Limited November 2019

+44 (0)1403 256941

A CIP catalogue record for this book is available at the British Library.

ISBN 978-1-84886-631-7

www.maverickbooks.co.uk

Yellow

This book is rated as: Yellow Band (Guided Reading)
This story is decodable at Letters and Sounds Phase 3/4.

Can I Have a Dragon?

by **Elizabeth Dale**

illustrated by
Ellie O'Shea

"Look at that rabbit!" said Dan.

"I love rabbits."

"Please can I have a pet rabbit?"

"Look at that cat," said Dan.

"Please can I have a pet cat?"

"Look at that dog," said Dan.

"Please can I have a pet dog?"

"Look at the dragon on that book," said Dan.

"I love dragons.

Please can I have a pet dragon?"

Dan was sad.

A dragon was the best pet of all.

They went into a toy shop.

"Please can I have a dragon's egg?"
said Dan.

17

"I love my dragon's egg," said Dan.

He hugged it all the way back.

Dan hugged the egg

as he had his fish and chips.

He hugged it all night long.

In the morning,

Dan had a big shock.

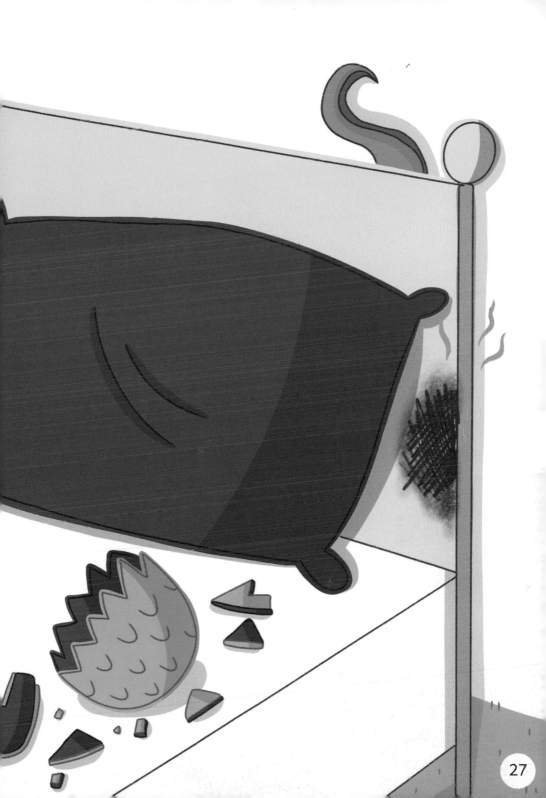

Quiz

1. What does Dan ask for first?
a) A rabbit
b) A turtle
c) A hamster

2. What does Dan see on a book?
a) A dog
b) A flower
c) A dragon

3. They went into a ____ shop.
a) Cat
b) Toy
c) Pet

4. Dan _____ it all the way back.
a) Kissed
b) Ran
c) Hugged

5. What happened in the morning?
a) Dan got a big shock
b) Dan got a dog
c) Dan got a cat

Turn over for answers

Book Bands for Guided Reading

The Institute of Education book banding system is a scale of colours that reflects the various levels of reading difficulty. The bands are assigned by taking into account the content, the language style, the layout and phonics. Word, phrase and sentence level work is also taken into consideration.

Maverick Early Readers are a bright, attractive range of books covering the pink to white bands. All of these books have been book banded for guided reading to the industry standard and edited by a leading educational consultant.

To view the whole Maverick Readers scheme, visit our website at

www.maverickearlyreaders.com

Or scan the QR code above to view our scheme instantly!

Quiz Answers: 1a, 2c, 3b, 4c, 5a